D1006488

ADAM BRADFORD, COWBOY

By
Donald Russell

Illustrations
Max Ranft

BENEFIC PRESS
Westchester, Illinois

Americans All Cowboy Series

Adam Bradford, Cowboy

Cowboy Without A Horse

Cowboy On The Mountain

Cowboy On The Trail

Editors,

Louisa Johnston and Joellen Reiter

Library of Congress
Number 73-91289

Contents

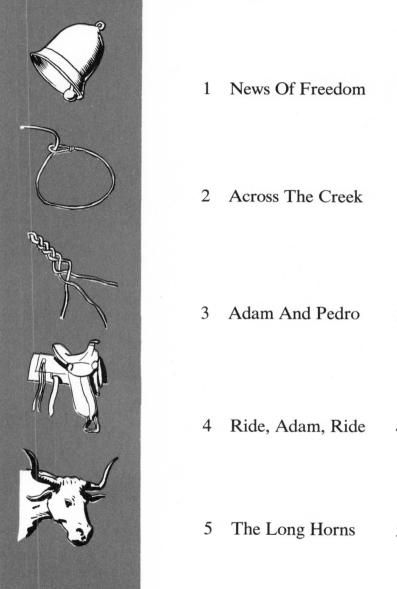

1 News Of Freedom   5

2 Across The Creek   17

3 Adam And Pedro   33

4 Ride, Adam, Ride   41

5 The Long Horns   51

1 News Of Freedom

Adam Bradford was a slave.
He was a slave on a farm.

Adam did not like being a slave, but he did not have to work very hard because the land on the farm was not good for growing things.

One year Adam had picked cotton. All the slaves had picked cotton.

There were many slaves on the farm. They picked cotton all day for many days.

The cotton was put in a wagon.
Then the men took it away. They
took the cotton where they could
get money for it.

The master said he did not
get much money for the cotton.
He said he would not try to
grow more cotton now.

Adam helped with the horses
on the farm. He fed the horses,
and he gave them water.

Sometimes he rode the horses.
He liked the horses, and he
liked to ride them. He learned
to be a good rider.

10

Adam's father and mother had a garden. Adam helped work in the garden. They had things to eat from the garden.

11

One morning a bell rang to call the slaves to work.

The master said, "We will not work this morning. You are free.

"You may go away if you wish. If you wish to stay, I will give you money. It will not be much for we have not had much to sell.

"But you may stay in your houses. And you will have food to eat.

"If you go away, you must work to get money for your food. You must work hard to get money for a house to live in.

"Maybe we will grow cotton again. Long-horned cows are in the woods. Maybe we can sell them. But it could be a long time before we can sell the cows.

"When I have money again, you will get some of it. Tell me if you want to stay."

Adam's father and mother talked about what the master had said.

"It would be good to go somewhere else," said Adam's mother. "I will not know I am free until I go away."

"We all feel that way," said Adam's father. "But if all of us go somewhere else, it will be hard to find work. There will be many people trying to find work."

"The master has been good," said Adam's father. "He has not whipped us. He helped us when we were ill. He let us have gardens. He let us have good food."

"He did all this because he owned us," said Adam's mother. "It was not because he was good. If we were ill, we could not work for him. He is as good to his horses as he is to us."

"But he has been good," said Adam's father. "We are free now, and we can come and go as we want."

"But if we go away, we may see some other farm we like," said Adam's mother. "We may find work there."

"But here we have a house to live in," said Adam's father. "Here we have food. We should stay for now."

2 Across The Creek

Adam had listened to his father and mother. He thought he would like to go somewhere else. He wished to feel that he were free.

The next morning he fed the horses. He gave them water.

Then he went to the big field where the cotton had been.

Adam crossed the big field.
He went into the woods. He
looked for long-horned cows.

18

"I do not like the long-horned cows," thought Adam. "If one comes near, I will hide."

Adam saw some of the long-horned cows, but they did not come near him.

Adam went down a steep hill. A creek was near the hill. The creek was at the end of the farm. Adam had not crossed it before. But this time he would cross the creek. Then he would feel free.

Adam went across the creek.
On the other side was a steep
hill. Adam went up the hill.

Then there was a *swish*!
Adam could not move. A rope was around him.

Adam looked up.

A boy was holding the other end of the rope.

"I have caught a runaway," said the boy holding the rope.

"I am not a runaway," said Adam. "I am free."

"You are not free to come on our land if we do not want you," said the boy.

"Will you let me come on your land?" asked Adam.

"I will," said the boy. "It is good to see you."

Adam looked at the boy. The boy had dark skin, but it was not as dark as Adam's.

"Are you a white boy?" Adam asked.

"Some people would tell you we are not," said the boy. "Some people call us Mexican. But my people were here long before there was a Mexico."

The boy went on, "My people were here before anyone came here from the United States. Some of my people were white Spanish people. Some of my people were Indians."

"Were you slaves?" Adam asked the boy.

"Some of my people were slaves," said the boy. "Spanish people made slaves of some Indians. But it is not good to be a slave."

"You are Spanish, but you talk just like me," said Adam. "I thought Spanish people had other words."

"My people are Spanish American," said the boy. "We talk in Spanish. But I learned to talk like you in school."

"What is a school like?" asked Adam.

"A school is a small house," said the boy. "A schoolmaster teaches you. When he rings a bell, you listen to him. You are there to learn."

The boy went on, "The schoolmaster whips boys who are not good. He whips boys who do not try to learn."

"Going to school must be like being a slave," said Adam.

"It is not," said the boy. "You learn many things. You learn to count. Then you could count the long-horned cows you see in the woods."

"You learn to write," said the boy. "Then you could write how many cows you saw. You could write how much money you could get for them.

"You learn to read," said the boy. "Then you can find out about far-away lands and far-away people."

"I would like to go to school," said Adam. "I would like to learn. But just now I would like to learn one thing. I would like to know how you put that long rope around me."

30

The boy said, "I made a loop at the end of my rope. I swung the rope around my head in a circle. Then I threw it so it came down over your head."

"I like that," said Adam. "Now I want to know how to use the rope. Will you teach me?"

32

3 Adam And Pedro

"We will have a school," said the boy. "I am Pedro. Now I will be Schoolmaster Pedro!"

"I am Adam," said Adam. "Now teach me."

"I will," said Pedro.

Pedro went away from the creek. He showed Adam a stump. Pedro swung the rope around his head and threw it.

The loop dropped over the stump. Pedro pulled the loop very tight.

He had caught the stump just as he had caught Adam!

"Now you try it, Adam," said Pedro.

Adam tried to swing the rope
around his head. But the loop
became very small.

When Adam threw the rope,
the loop did not go over
the stump.

35

"That was a good try, Adam," said Pedro. "Now try again."

Adam tried again. This time he threw a big loop, but the loop went way over the stump.

Adam tried again and again. But the loop did not go over the stump.

One time the loop dropped over the stump. Adam pulled the loop tight.

"Good!" called Pedro.

"Now you know you can do
it," said Pedro. "You must go
on trying until you can do it
every time. But you must have
your own rope. Let me tell
you how to make one."

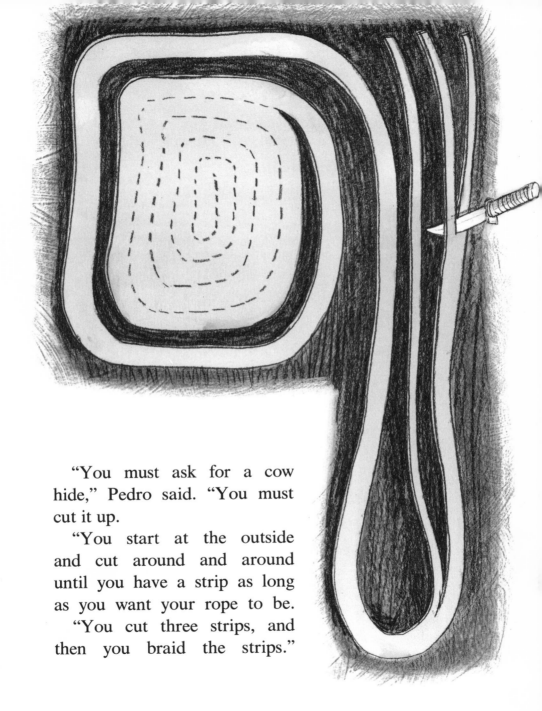

"You must ask for a cow hide," Pedro said. "You must cut it up.

"You start at the outside and cut around and around until you have a strip as long as you want your rope to be.

"You cut three strips, and then you braid the strips."

"How do you braid, Pedro?" asked Adam.

"Like this," said Pedro.

"That is not men's work," said Adam.

Pedro said, "It is when you can make a rope that will hold one of the long-horned cows."

4 Ride, Adam, Ride

When Adam went to his house, he told his father about Pedro. He told his father about the rope made of cow hide.

Adam's father said he could get a cow hide to make a rope.

The next day Adam went to get his cow hide. Then he started cutting a long strip of the hide.

Adam cut around and around until he had a strip as long as Pedro's rope. Then he cut some more strips. His sister, Ann, helped him braid the strips into a rope.

Adam tied one end of the rope into a small circle and pulled it tight. Then he put the other end of the rope into the circle and pulled it up to make a loop.

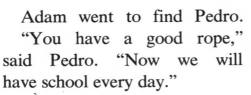

Adam went to find Pedro. "You have a good rope," said Pedro. "Now we will have school every day."

Pedro showed Adam how to throw his rope. After many tries, Adam could throw the loop over the stump every time.

44

Every morning Adam fed the
horses. Some days he would be
told to take a horse to the
field. Then Adam would ride
the horse there.

One day when he was riding
a horse to the field, he saw
the master.

The master said, "Adam,
do you like to ride?"

"I like to ride very much,"
said Adam.

"That is good, Adam," the master said. "I will tell Ben to let you ride a horse every day. I will tell Ben to let you use a saddle.

"Ben will show you how to put a saddle on a horse."

Every day after that Adam rode a horse.

Some of the horses jumped and bucked. Sometimes a horse threw Adam off.

But Adam learned to stay in the saddle when the horse jumped and bucked.

Adam went for long rides. On one of his long rides, he went to see Pedro.

"It is good to see you, Adam," said Pedro. "Now we will have school again. You must learn to throw the rope while you ride. You must try to rope a calf.

"When you get your rope over a calf, you must tie the end of your rope around the horn on your saddle.

"Then you stop your horse. When the calf gets to the end of the rope, it will stop. Then you get off your horse and tie up the calf."

Adam threw the loop many
times before he caught a calf.
But soon he could rope a
calf every time he threw the loop.

5　The Long Horns

One day the master called all the men who worked on the farm to come to his house.

The master said, "I am told that we can sell our long-horned cows. But we must drive them a long way.

"We must drive the cows to the end of the railroad. The railroad is in Kansas."

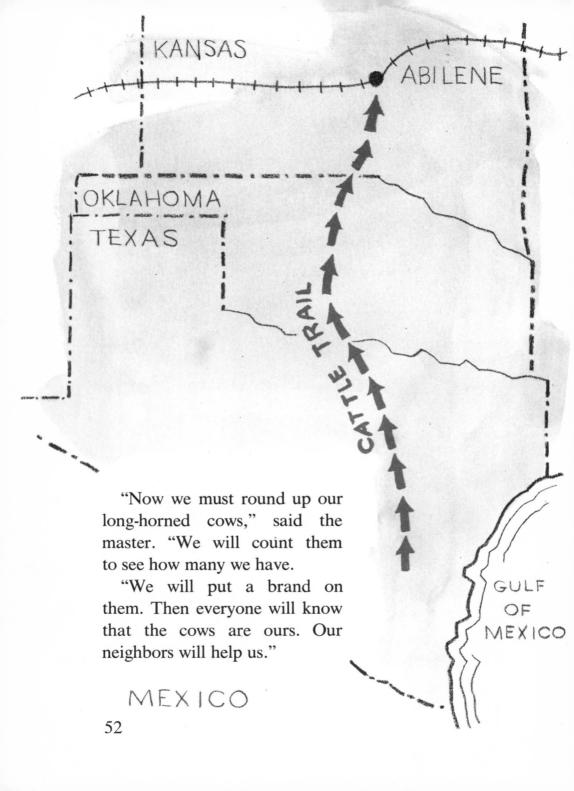

KANSAS

ABILENE

OKLAHOMA

TEXAS

CATTLE TRAIL

"Now we must round up our long-horned cows," said the master. "We will count them to see how many we have.

"We will put a brand on them. Then everyone will know that the cows are ours. Our neighbors will help us."

GULF
OF
MEXICO

MEXICO

52

After three days, all the neighbors came riding up to the master's house.

Then the men rode their horses to the woods. They made a line across one side of the woods.

Adam and Pedro rode with
the men. They had their
ropes with them.

The men rode into the woods.
They made all the cows go
out of the woods and into
the field.

Then the men made a big circle around the cows in the field. One long-horned cow ran away from the other cows.

The long-horned cow ran
near the master.

Adam rode his horse after the long-horned cow. He swung his rope around his head. He threw the rope and caught the long-horned cow.

57

Adam tied the end of his rope around the saddle horn. Adam's horse stopped.

The cow ran to the end of the rope and stopped.

Pedro rode up to the cow. He threw his rope around the cow's legs.

58

The long-horned cow could not move.

"Good boy, Adam," Pedro called. "You are a *vaquero*."

"What do you mean, Pedro?" asked Adam.

"I mean that you are a *cowboy*," said Pedro.

Vocabulary

The words used in this book should be familiar to pupils reading at the second grade level. For those pupils reading at the second grade level, special emphasis should be placed on the words below. The number indicates the page on which the word first appears.

braid 39	long-horned 12
brand 52	loop 31
bucked 48	
creek 17	runaway 23
ill 15	slave 5

vaquero 59

The Way To Say It

Some words are made by putting two small words together. What small words were put together to make these words?

became	into	railroad
cowboy	maybe	sometimes
everyone	runaway	somewhere

Find the words in the story.

Some words we use are from another place. Pedro told Adam about a Spanish word. The word was *vaquero*. It means cowboy.

Some words are like each other because they rhyme. You can use words that rhyme to make a poem. Some words from the story rhyme. They can be used to make up poems about Adam and Pedro.

Into the saddle, Adam's up and away.
Ride, Cowboy Adam, this is your day.
Pedro is someone you want to know.
He throws his rope and gives a good show.

Write a poem of your own about Adam and Pedro.

You And They

This is a short list of ways in which Adam and Pedro were alike.

Adam	Pedro
Boy	Boy
Born on a farm	Born on a farm
Liked horses	Liked horses

Put both names on a piece of paper and list some other ways in which the boys were alike.

Things To Know

Read this and make a list telling what things Adam and Pedro needed to know to be able to do what they did.

One day Adam and Pedro went for a ride on their horses. They rode for a long time. After awhile they saw some cows in the woods. They knew the cows should not be there.

Adam rode into the woods. He called to the cows. Soon the cows ran out of the woods. Adam and Pedro made them go back to the farm.

A calf tried to get away. Pedro threw his rope. It went over the calf's head. Soon the calf was on the ground. Pedro and Adam took it back to the farm with the other cows.

What things did Adam and Pedro need to know? Would you like to know some of the things they knew? What things would they be? How would you use them?

How To Do It

Adam wanted to be a cowboy. He had to learn many things to be a good cowboy. These are some of the things he learned. Copy the lines on a piece of paper and write in the missing words from the word list below.

Adam learned to throw a XXXX.
Adam learned to XXXXXX a horse.
Adam learned to rope XXXX.
To learn all this Adam had to XXXX.

saddle   cows   rope   work

What do you want to be? What will you need to learn to do it?

You Can Do It

In the story, Adam learned to braid a rope. Cowboys sometimes made their ropes this way.

Boys and girls can make a braided belt or neckpiece. These can be made with long, thin strips of colored plastic, cloth, or ribbon.

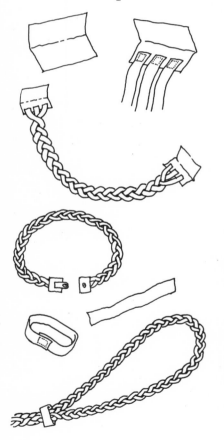

This is the way you do it.

Attach the ends of three long, thin strips of plastic, cloth, or ribbon to a small folded piece of the same material.

Now braid the strips as shown to the length needed.

Fold another piece of the same material and attach it to the free end of the strips.

A snap attached to the ends may be used to fasten the belt or neckpiece. Or a small loop of material may be made. Fasten both ends of the material together to make a ring. The two ends of a long neckpiece or belt may be held together in this way.